Working With
The
Mental Capacity Act 2005

Written by

Steven Richards *BA (Hons)* & Aasya F Mughal *LLB (Hons), Barrister*

www.matrixtrainingassociates.com

First published in 2006 by

Matrix Training Associates
2 The Green
North Waltham
Hampshire RG25 2BQ

British Library Cataloguing in Publication Data
A catalogue record for this book is available from the British Library

ISBN 978-0-9552349-0-3

Printed and bound in England

www.matrixtrainingassociates.com

Contents

Introduction

The Mental Capacity Act 2005 provides, for the first time, a statutory framework for assessing whether a person has capacity to make decisions and defines how others can make decisions on behalf of someone who lacks capacity.

Its scope is wide-ranging, involving decisions regarding personal welfare (care and treatment) and financial affairs. The Act directly addresses the issue of providing care and treatment for people who lack capacity. Prior to the Act being introduced such decisions have fundamentally lacked any legal protection unless taken to the courts on a case-by-case basis.

The Act works in three ways – providing protection, giving powers and defining duties:

Protection
The Act provides protection for people whose capacity is called into question. At present it is not uncommon for people to be labelled as lacking capacity to make decisions based purely on their diagnosis, such as dementia. For these people the Act provides protection by asserting the fundamental right that no matter what a person's diagnosis or behaviour they must be assumed to have capacity. Any doubt over a person's capacity must be proven and this can only be done by following the procedures laid down in the Act.

For people who do lack capacity, the Act provides protection by setting out a mandatory procedure for making decisions on their behalf. This is based on the decisions the people themselves may have made if they had been able to do so (best interest decisions). The Act also introduces a new criminal offence for the neglect or ill-treatment of those who lack capacity. Finally, for the most vulnerable people, the Act provides an independent support service (advocacy).

In addition to protecting people with reduced capacity, the Act also provides protection for the staff and carers working with them. The current situation (pre April 2007) gives no protection. For example, some people are prescribed and given medication when they do not have the capacity to consent because staff take the decision that this is the best thing to do. However, such actions have no legal protection and are open to court proceedings. On the other hand staff sometimes will not make decisions about treatment because the person lacks capacity to consent and staff may feel unsure about taking the decision for them. The Act resolves both these situations by providing a mechanism for making decisions on behalf of people who lack capacity and by giving legal protection to staff acting on these decisions.

Powers
The Act provides two fundamental powers in terms of personal welfare (care and treatment) decisions.

For people who have capacity it is the power to plan ahead for a time when they may lack capacity. At present there is no statutory mechanism for this in terms of future care and treatment. Following the implementation of the

Working With The Mental Capacity Act 2005

Act people will be able to assign another person to make care and treatment decisions on their behalf if they lose capacity to do so themselves in the future (lasting power of attorney). People will also be able to record their wishes for future treatment, especially the refusal of treatment, through an 'advance decision'. The Act provides a standard procedure to do this and formally recognises its authority.

The second power concerns staff and others working with people who lack capacity. This is the power to make decisions on behalf of another person who lacks capacity to consent. The Act provides a standard method for staff to make a 'best interests' decision and gives the authority for these decisions to be acted upon. The result should be better and more timely decisions on behalf of people lacking capacity with regard to their personal welfare.

Duties
The protection and powers mentioned above are only accessible by following the Act. Anyone working with people with reduced capacity is obliged to follow the rules and procedures laid down in the Act to benefit from it. They will have to provide evidence of doing this in their work. Statutory and non-statutory organisations providing health and social care for people who lack capacity will have to ensure that their policies and procedures take account of the Act. As a body they must comply with the legal requirements the Act places upon them. Managers will have to ensure staff have an understanding of the Act and can use the powers provided correctly. The Healthcare Commission and Commission of Social Care Inspection are likely to monitor and audit compliance with the Act from 2007.

Implementation of the Act

The Act is due to come into force in England and Wales in April 2007. Scotland already has its own legislation in place (Adults with Incapacity (Scotland) Act 2000).

The Act applies to adults aged 16 years and over. The one exception to this is discussed under *Age Exception* (page 34).

In addition to the Act there will be a number of parliamentary regulations and a code of practice that will provide more detail on the practical operation of the legislation. These are due to be completed before April 2007 and they will be accessible via: http://www.dca.gov.uk/menincap/legis.htm#bill

Interpretation

As with all legislation the Act is open to interpretation. Following the Act's implementation in April 2007 some cases, inevitably, will go before the Court of Protection. The outcome of these proceedings should clarify parts of the Act, its precise operation and implementation.

This guide provides a detailed explanation of the Mental Capacity Act, however it should not be regarded as a substitute for the Act itself. Nothing in it is intended to be, or should be, relied upon as legal advice.

The guide follows the format of the Act and uses the masculine form (he/his) throughout.

Practical Information

Who will be directly affected?

The Act will directly affect all those who have reduced capacity to make decisions. This will include people with dementia, severe learning disabilities, severe brain injuries, mental health problems, autism and other conditions. The number of people affected is forecast to be two million. From April 2007 this population will immediately come under the remit of the Act and any staff working with them will also become bound by the duties the Act places upon them.

Where will the Act be used?

The Act relates to any decision involving people who have reduced capacity. These decisions can be financial or related to care and treatment and are not restricted to any one environment. As a result of its wide ranging remit the Act will be operational in a person's home, in hospitals (both medical and mental health), in care homes, in supported housing, in general practitioners' (GPs) surgeries and dental practices.

Which staff will be affected by the Act?

All staff that work with people with reduced capacity will be directly affected by the Act. The list of staff is extensive and includes GPs, district nurses, practice nurses, social workers, care managers, psychologists, consultants, dentists, occupational therapists, physiotherapists, care home staff, hospital staff and doctors. In addition relatives, carers, advocates and people who work for voluntary services will be affected by, and required to use, the Act if they are involved with people who have reduced capacity.

The government estimates that this will be as many as six million people (health and social care staff and informal carers).

How does the Act affect existing guidance on capacity?

From April 2007 the Act will supersede all existing guidance on capacity. Its authority as statute means that any codes of practice, guidance or policies (British Medical Association, Royal College of Nursing, Department of Health or Social Services) that do not follow its requirements will be invalid.

Any service or person working with someone who lacks capacity will have to follow the Act and, as with any legislation, there is no excuse for not knowing about it or not having information on it. A lack of knowledge of the Act will not be accepted as a valid defence in law.

Note

The Mental Capacity Act 2005, in common with all legislation, is arranged into a number of parts which are called 'Sections'. Each Section has a number and these are referred to in this guide where appropriate. Every Section of the Act is listed at the back of the guide (page 42).

Key Parts of the Act

- **Principles** – five principles that underpin the entire Act and provide a safeguard for people whose capacity is called into question.

- **Capacity test** – a standard test to assess a person's capacity that is based on the decision-making process and can be used by professionals and non-professionals alike.

- **Decision-making** – a procedure for others to make decisions on behalf of people who lack capacity concerning their care, treatment and finances.

- **Restraint** – provision for the lawful restraint of a person who lacks capacity, when certain criteria are met.

- **Advance decisions** – a legal mechanism to allow people with capacity to plan ahead and state future decisions about treatment, including the refusal of life-sustaining treatment.

- **Lasting powers of attorney** – people with capacity will be able to appoint another person to make care, treatment and financial decisions on their behalf in the future. They replace the existing system of enduring powers of attorney.

- **Advocacy** – the creation of independent mental capacity advocates to provide a safeguard for the most vulnerable people affected by the Act.

- **Payments** – rules to guide payments made by others on behalf of people who lack capacity.

- **Court of Protection** – the judicial body that will act as the main arbiter on disputed and complex decisions concerning the Act. It replaces the previous, more limited, Court of Protection.

- **Deputies** – people appointed by the Court of Protection to help make decisions on behalf of people who lack capacity. They replace the present system of court appointed receivers.

- **Public Guardian** – will register and supervise the work of lasting powers of attorneys and deputies. It replaces the current Public Guardianship Office.

- **Research** – powers and procedures that allow for and safeguard research involving people who lack capacity.

- **Code of practice** – a statutory code covering the Act and providing detailed guidance on its use.

- **Criminal offence** – a new offence concerning the ill-treatment or neglect of people who lack capacity, punishable by imprisonment.

The Principles (Section 1)

The Act starts with five principles. These are the foundations of the entire legislation. Everyone using the Act or involved with it must follow the principles in every action and decision they make. The principles can be seen as a set of rights for people whose capacity is called into question.

The principles:

When assessing capacity:

1. A person must be assumed to have capacity UNLESS it is proved otherwise.

   and

2. Until all practicable steps have been taken to help someone make a decision without success they CANNOT be treated as lacking capacity.

   and

3. An unwise decision does NOT in itself indicate a lack of capacity.

When acting or making decisions on behalf of someone lacking capacity:

4. Any act or decision made must be in the person's best interests.

   and

5. Any act or decision must be the least restrictive option to the person in terms of their rights and freedom of action.

Additional information

Principle 1 – the burden of proof as to whether someone lacks capacity falls on those assessing the person. If staff consider that a person does not have capacity to make a decision on a matter, the Act requires that they provide proof of this. This proof will come from completing the test for capacity, which the Act lays out in Section 3 (page 7).

Principle 2 – the Act requires staff to help and support someone, they consider to lack capacity, to see if with appropriate help they can make a decision. Again, evidence of providing help and support will need to be shown.

Principle 3 – the Act allows people to make, what may be seen to be, irrational or eccentric decisions and still have capacity. Fundamentally, this supports and protects people who make decisions that others do not agree with and which are seen as unwise.

Principle 4 – the term 'best interests' is defined and expanded upon in Section 4 (page 9).

Defining Capacity (Section 2)

The Act defines a lack of capacity as follows:

> "..a person lacks capacity in relation to a matter if at **the material time** he is unable to make a decision for himself **in relation to the matter** because of an **impairment of, or a disturbance** in the functioning of, the mind or brain."

This definition contains a number of important elements that must be taken into account when deciding if a person lacks capacity.

Time specific ("the material time")

An assessment of capacity must be time specific. The issue is whether a person has capacity to make a decision at a specific time. This recognises that capacity can fluctuate over time. In using the Act staff must assess a person's capacity at the time a decision is required.

Decision specific ("in relation to the matter")

An assessment of capacity relates to a specific decision that has to be made and it is NOT about a general ability to make decisions. For example, a person may not have capacity to make complex investment decisions but may have the capacity to pay their household bills.

Diagnostic threshold ("impairment of, or a disturbance")

For a person to lack capacity they must have a medically recognised impairment of, or disturbance in the functioning of, the mind or brain. Examples include psychiatric illness, learning disability, dementia, toxic confusional state and physical trauma to the brain. The lack of capacity can be of a temporary or permanent nature.

Age, appearance, condition or behaviour

A lack of capacity cannot be decided merely by reference to a person's age, appearance, condition or behaviour. For example, someone who has an established learning disability with severe behavioural problems does not necessarily lack capacity.

Balance of probabilities

In using the Act any question over a lack of capacity must be decided on the balance of probabilities, that is, what is more likely than not.

Assessing Capacity (Section 3)

Having defined capacity, the Act provides a test for assessing whether a person has capacity to make a decision. This test is central to the entire legislation and the single most important Section. It is the gateway to the majority of the powers provided by the Act. If a person fails the test and is therefore deemed to lack capacity, the rest of the Act can be accessed.

The test is a 'functional' assessment which looks at the decision-making process rather than the outcome. It is designed to be carried out by anyone - there is no requirement for a doctor or another clinician to be involved. Given the wide remit of the Act, especially in terms of personal welfare decisions, it is likely that carers and others who do not work for statutory services, and are not professionally qualified, will carry out many assessments. Primarily it is for the person who requires a decision to make the assessment.

There are four parts to the test and failure on any part indicates a lack of capacity.

To have capacity to make a decision someone must be able to:

---

1. understand the information relevant to the decision.

   and

2. retain the information.

   and

3. use or weigh the information to arrive at a choice.

   and

4. communicate the decision.

Additional information

<u>Understand the information</u>
The test as to whether someone understands the information relevant to the decision places a requirement on those making the assessment to help the person understand the information. Information should be presented in a way that is appropriate to the individual concerned, for example using simple language or visual aids. It is acceptable for the information to be understood at a simple level and in broad terms. The draft code of practice to the Act gives further examples of the support that should be considered. For example, using people the person knows well and trusts to communicate the information and considering the best time and location for doing so.

<u>Retain the information</u>
The information only has to be retained long enough to make the decision. It could be forgotten an hour later and the decision would still be valid. If a person has problems retaining information staff should consider ways to help address this.

<u>Use or weigh the information</u>
In order to be able to use or weigh information a person must first believe the information presented. For example, a person with bi-polar disorder (manic depression) may, during a period of illness, consider they are immortal and not susceptible to any illness. In terms of the assessment above they may understand and retain the information to make a decision about treatment, however, they would not believe the treatment to be necessary and so would be assessed as lacking capacity. A person must also be able to consider and balance the arguments for and against a proposed course of action before making a decision. These arguments would include any probable consequences of deciding one way or another or of failing to make a decision.

<u>Communicate the decision</u>
The decision can be communicated by any method recognised by those making the assessment, for example hand signals or blinks. If communication is limited then those undertaking the assessment should employ a specialist worker to ensure that a person's capacity is not incorrectly judged simply because no one could recognise their means of communication.

Reasonable belief

To reach a conclusion, based on this assessment, it is sufficient that the person making the assessment holds a "reasonable belief" that someone either has or lacks capacity with regard to a particular decision. Absolute certainty is not therefore required. However, the person making the assessment would need to be able to give objective reasons for their belief.

Involving professionals

There may be certain situations where it would be beneficial to involve professionals in assessments that would not normally require them. Possible examples might include cases where there is disagreement among family members as to a person's capacity, or where there are legal consequences to a finding of capacity or where the person concerned is giving different decisions to different people.

Refusal to be assessed

The draft code of practice considers the issue of people who are unable or unwilling to engage in the assessment process. Its view is that if the person concerned is unable to engage fully but is compliant with the process, and staff feel that it is in the person's best interests to enable them to make a personal welfare or financial decision, then it would be appropriate to carry out the assessment. However, if the person is unwilling to engage in the process and has capacity they can refuse to be assessed under the Act and no assessment can take place.

Working With The Mental Capacity Act 2005

Making Decisions for People who Lack Capacity (Sections 4-5)

Once a person is assessed as lacking capacity to make a specific decision, the Act allows another person involved in the matter to make a 'best interests' decision on their behalf. Section 4 provides a checklist that must be followed when making a best interests decision. The list is not exhaustive and so other factors may also be considered. It does, however, provide a mandatory starting point, which will ensure a uniform approach to all cases. When going through the checklist the focus must be on the person lacking capacity rather than the decision-maker's own personal views. That is, the decision-maker must ask what the person who lacks capacity would have wanted.

To make a 'best interests' decision the decision-maker must:

1. consider all the relevant circumstances.
   and
2. consider whether it is likely that the person may have capacity at some time in the future to the matter in question. The decision could then be delayed so that the person could make it themselves.
   and
3. encourage, as far as is reasonably practicable, the person to participate in any action undertaken for him or in any decision affecting him. Even where the person lacks capacity, they should not be excluded from the decision-making process.
   and
4. not be motivated by a desire to bring about the person's death when the decision relates to life-sustaining treatment. (This does NOT mean doctors are under an obligation to provide or continue life-sustaining treatment when that treatment is NOT in the best interests of the person.)
   and
5. consider the person's past and present wishes and feelings.
   and
6. consider any relevant written statement made when the person had capacity.
   and
7. consider the beliefs and values that would be likely to influence the person's decision, for example, religious, cultural and lifestyle choices.
   and
8. take into account other factors the person would be likely to consider if he were able to do so. For example, emotional bonds or family obligations in deciding how to spend money or where to live.
   and
9. consult and take into account the views of other key people as to what would be in the person's best interests including: anyone named by the person to be consulted, any carer or person interested in his welfare (family, friends, informal carers, professionals or voluntary services including an existing advocate), any lasting power of attorney or any deputy appointed by the Court of Protection.

Age, appearance, condition or behaviour

The Act clearly states the above checklist must be followed and moreover adds that the decision-maker cannot decide what is in a person's best interests based merely on their age, appearance, condition or behaviour.

Additional information

While the checklist is fairly self-explanatory, the draft code of practice expands on some of the points. It states that:

- No priority should be attached to any one numbered consideration within the list.

- Past and present wishes and feelings may not necessarily be verbally expressed. Emotional responses and other behaviour may be judged as evidence of a person's wishes and feelings. The use of an independent advocate to provide support in assessing such factors should be considered.

Advance decisions

If the person has made an advance decision relating to the decision in question, this will override this Section of the Act and therefore the need to carry out a best interests assessment. See *Advance Decisions* (page 15).

Decisions covered by the Act

The Act covers financial and personal welfare decisions on behalf of people who lack capacity. Further information about financial decisions and the scope of such decisions is given later in the guide. However it is worth noting at this point that the term "personal welfare decisions", as used in the Act, embraces a very broad spectrum of care related decisions. The following examples illustrate just how many services will be affected:

- care given to people including washing, dressing, doing their shopping and taking them to appointments,
- care provided by services such as occupational therapy, physiotherapy, chiropody, nursing care (in the community and in hospitals), community dentistry and supported housing,
- social care services provided by voluntary organisations,
- any medical treatment, including diagnostic tests,
- the movement of someone to a care home or another type of accommodation and
- contact a person has with other people. See *Court of Protection* (page 24).

There are some healthcare decisions however that are always likely to require referral to the Court of Protection. Present information indicates at least two decisions will be named prior to April 2007. These are the withholding or withdrawal of artificial nutrition and hydration from patients in a permanent vegetative state and the non-therapeutic sterilisation of a person lacking capacity to consent.

Who makes the decision?

The person involved in the matter may be informal, such as a family member, or formal such as a professional who is seeking a decision.

Least restrictive principle

It is worth noting that principle 5 (page 5) states that any best interests decision should be the least restrictive option available. Any restrictions to a person's rights and freedoms, which are a consequence of an act or decision, are therefore kept to a minimum. There may be an alternative way of acting which is just as effective but less restrictive. In these circumstances, this alternative should be used. The decision-maker must also consider whether it is necessary to act at all.

Consulting others

The obligation to consult others only applies if it is "practicable and appropriate" to do so. In an emergency it may not be possible to consult with anyone. However, for a series of non-urgent minor decisions that taken together have a significant effect, consultation would be required.

Disputes

It will be the case that some decisions are not clear cut and involve conflicting views from those involved. In such cases the decision-maker should try and reach a consensus. However, ultimately it is the decision-maker who is responsible for determining the best interests decision and they may have to make a decision that not everyone involved agrees with.

If people do not agree that the decision-maker has made the correct best interests decision, they can challenge it by applying to the Court of Protection (page 24).

Protection for the decision-maker

By considering all the above factors when determining what would be in the person's best interests, the decision-maker is protected by the Act. It acknowledges that the decision-maker can only consider circumstances he is aware of and which could reasonably be regarded as relevant. The decision made could, with hindsight, be discovered to have been incorrect and the decision-maker may be challenged. However, he is protected as long as he is able to show he followed the checklist and acted within the boundaries of the Act.

Legal authority of a best interests decision

A person that follows the procedure for making a best interests decision involving care or treatment on behalf of someone lacking capacity is protected from liability. It would have been as if the person in question had had capacity and had consented to the decision. However a person is not protected from liability for loss or damage as a result of negligence in carrying out the agreed action.

Restraint (Section 6)

The Act allows for the lawful restraint of a person lacking capacity. Restraint is defined as:

> the use or threat of force to make a person do something they are resisting.
>
> **or**
>
> the restriction of liberty of movement, whether or not the person resists.

Within this definition, restraint could be verbal or physical and may involve threatening a person with an action, holding them down or locking them in a room. It also includes chemical restraint such as sedation.

Criteria needed for restraint

> 1. The person lacks capacity to the matter in question and it will be in the person's best interests (Section 4) for the act to be done.
>   **and**
> 2. It is reasonable to believe that it is necessary to restrain the person to prevent harm to them.
>   **and**
> 3. The restraint is a proportionate response to the likelihood of the person suffering harm and the seriousness of that harm.

Additional information

The third criterion, a proportionate response, is one that represents the minimum force necessary for the shortest possible time.

The onus falls on the person carrying out the restraint (or authorising it) to identify the reasons which justify it, for example, the person would suffer harm unless they were restrained in some way.

Restraint may be required, for example, if someone lacking capacity resists the use of a seat belt when being taken to a necessary appointment. The Act would allow for their restraint to fasten the seat belt during the journey if the above criteria were met.

Lasting powers of attorney

An attorney may authorise someone else to restrain the person, in particular circumstances, if the criteria were met.

Court appointed deputies

A court appointed deputy cannot authorise the restraint of a person unless the criteria above are met and they have authority for restraint conferred on them by the Court of Protection. That being the case, a deputy may also authorise someone else to restrain the person.

Prior instructions on restraint

If a person has a lasting power of attorney or there is a court appointed deputy whose scope of authority covers this area and either the attorney or deputy have given prior instructions, then these cannot be over-ridden.

However, if the attorney's or deputy's instruction would stop a person receiving life-sustaining treatment or lead to a serious deterioration in their condition, then the staff involved could ignore the instruction while a decision is sought from the Court of Protection. This would not be necessary however if the deputy already had authority with regard to the person's treatment.

Restraint v deprivation of liberty

Restraint, as allowed for in the Mental Capacity Act, permits the restriction of a person's liberty of movement, if certain criteria are met. However it does NOT permit any act that deprives a person of his liberty within the meaning of Article 5(1) of the European Convention on Human Rights (ECHR).

This limitation echoes the case of <u>HL v United Kingdom (45508/99) 2004</u>, which has become more commonly known as the 'Bournewood Judgment' and is considered in more detail below.

<u>The Case</u>
'HL', an adult male, lacked the capacity to consent to admission to hospital or his subsequent stay in hospital. However, when HL became unwell and it was felt that he needed hospital care, the decision was taken to admit him informally (as a voluntary patient) as he showed no intention of leaving and was not resisting being on the ward. However, when HL's carers wanted to discharge him, the hospital refused. Their refusal was challenged through legal proceedings.

<u>The Law</u>
The European Convention on Human Rights provides the following with regards to deprivation of liberty:

Article 5(1):
  "Everyone has the right to liberty and security of person. No one shall be deprived of liberty save in the following cases (below at 5(1)(e) *and in accordance with a procedure prescribed by law"*

Article 5(1)(e):
  "The lawful detention of persons for the prevention of the spreading of infectious diseases, of persons of unsound mind, alcoholics or drug addicts or vagrants."

Article 5(4):

> *"Everyone who is deprived of his liberty by arrest or detention shall be entitled to take proceedings by which the lawfulness of his detention shall be decided speedily by a court and his release ordered if the detention is not lawful."*

<u>The Judgment</u>

It was decided in the European Court of Human Rights, that there had been a violation of Article 5(1)(e), because there was a lack of effective procedure to determine the admission and detention of HL as a compliant incapacitated individual. HL had been deprived of his liberty because the healthcare professionals in charge of his care had complete control over his assessment, care, treatment and residence. HL was under constant supervision and was not free to leave.

Furthermore, because domestic law did not provide HL with an effective means by which the lawfulness of his detention could be reviewed, there had also been a violation of Article 5(4).

In one respect the Mental Capacity Act does resolve part of this case. It provides a means to admit a person lacking capacity to hospital (or other place) through a best interests decision. However, what it does NOT allow for is the detention of a person lacking capacity.

Advance Decisions to Refuse Treatment (Sections 24-26)

The terms 'advance directives' and 'living wills' may already be familiar to readers of this guide. The Act replaces these with the term 'advance decisions' and provides a clear procedure for making such decisions. An advance decision is essentially a statement made by a person with capacity detailing their wishes in relation to future treatment decisions they may face at a time when they lack capacity. It is a means of planning ahead.

The Act asserts the legal authority of advance decisions and makes it clear that they must be followed by medical staff and others when dealing with people who lack capacity.

Requirements

Advance decisions can only be made by a person who has capacity and is 18 years or over.

A specified treatment or situation may be expressed in lay person's terms, for example "do not put me on a machine that breathes for me", and it will still be valid.

A person can withdraw or alter an advance decision at any time provided he has the capacity to do so. Such a withdrawal or alteration in the decision does not need to be in writing.

Life-sustaining treatment

An advance decision can only apply to the refusal of life-sustaining treatment if:

1. it is in writing. (This can include being written in medical notes and electronic records. It does not have to be physically written by the person themselves.)
   and
2. it is signed by the person or by someone else in the person's presence as directed by them.
   and
3. the signature is made or acknowledged by the person in the presence of a witness.
   and
4. the witness signs it or acknowledges his signature in the person's presence.
   and
5. the decision is verified with a statement that it applies to that treatment even if life is at risk.

Advance decisions that do not extend to life-sustaining treatment

An advance decision that does not include the refusal of life-sustaining treatment does not have to meet the requirements above. It does not have to be written and in fact there is no particular format required by the Act.

An advance decision is NOT valid if:

1. a lasting power of attorney was created after the advance decision, which gave the attorney authority to give or refuse consent to treatment to which the advance decision relates. However, the existence of any other form of lasting power of attorney will not invalidate the advance decision.

2. the person has clearly acted in a way contrary to the advance decision. (For example, if a Jehovah's Witness makes an advance decision stating they do not wish to receive blood transfusions and later converts to the Baptist Church, this would call into question the validity of the advance decision if it remained unchanged.)

3. at the time of treatment the person has capacity to give or refuse consent.

4. the treatment planned is not specified in the advance decision.

5. any circumstances specified in the advance decision are absent.

6. there are reasonable grounds to believe that circumstances have changed to such an extent that they would have affected the original decision. For example, new medication that radically changes the outlook for a particular condition.

Legal authority of advance decisions

A valid advance decision to refuse treatment has the same authority as if the person had had capacity and refused treatment. It will therefore take precedence over a decision by the Court of Protection, a court appointed deputy, a lasting power of attorney (that was made before the date of the advance decision) and a best interests decision by the treatment team involved.

Those treating a person will not incur any liability for following an advance decision. That is the case even if, in accordance with the advance decision, they withdraw or withhold treatment provided they reasonably believe the advance decision is valid and applicable to the treatment.

Exemptions

An individual may give treatment to a person unaware that a valid advance decision exists. However, as soon as they become aware of such a decision and provided there is no dispute as to its validity, then the decision must be followed or the person giving treatment becomes liable for their actions.

If the person giving treatment disputes the advance decision, for example questioning its existence, validity or applicability to the treatment, then the case should be referred to the Court of Protection. In the meantime, treatment can be continued.

Mental Health Act 1983

An advance decision does NOT override the powers of the Mental Health Act 1983. People who are detained under this Act can be given treatment for a mental disorder without consent and advance decisions will not apply. However, the Mental Health Act 1983 does not extend to medical treatment for any other conditions, so a person detained under the Act could still have a valid advance decision in relation to medical treatment decisions.

Lasting Powers of Attorney (Sections 9-14)

This part of the Act provides another means for people to plan ahead for a time when they may lack capacity. An individual (the donor) makes the power when they have capacity and it gives another person (the donee) authority to make decisions on the donor's behalf, when they are unable to do so for themselves.

There is an important distinction to be made between financial lasting powers of attorney and personal welfare (care and treatment) lasting powers of attorney. With the former, the person making the lasting power of attorney can give control of their finances to an attorney before or after they lose capacity. With the latter, control over decisions can only be given when the person lacks capacity.

Lasting powers of attorney replace the current system of enduring powers of attorney which are restricted to financial matters only.

Requirements

To make a lasting power of attorney the person must be at least 18 years and have capacity.

The person making the lasting power of attorney may impose conditions and restrictions on it. For example, they may wish to specify that the lasting power of attorney only deals with financial matters.

Rules for attorneys

An attorney must be 18 years or over. If the power relates to property and financial affairs, the attorney could be a trust corporation.

A bankrupt person cannot be a lasting power of attorney in relation to property and financial affairs.

More than one person may act as an attorney for someone by acting either jointly or severally. If acting jointly, both attorneys must agree each decision made. If acting severally, any of the attorneys appointed can make decisions unilaterally without the involvement of the others.

Substitute or successor attorneys

An attorney cannot appoint a substitute or successor but the person making the lasting power of attorney can make provision to change their attorney following specific events, for example:

- the attorney renouncing his role,
- the attorney's death,
- the attorney's insolvency,
- the divorce or termination of a civil partnership between the attorney and the person who made the lasting power of attorney or
- the attorney losing capacity to act.

Working With The Mental Capacity Act 2005

Obligation to the Act

An attorney must comply with the principles (Section 1) and best interests (Section 4) of the Act when making decisions on behalf of the person they represent. For example they should consult, where appropriate, relatives, carers and others when making decisions as indicated in the best interests checklist (page 9).

Personal welfare decisions

Where the donor authorises the attorney to make personal welfare decisions, these decisions:

1. are restricted to decisions where the person lacks capacity.
2. are subject to advance decisions made after the lasting power of attorney.
3. can include giving or refusing consent to healthcare treatment.
4. can include giving or refusing consent to life-sustaining treatment.

Duties of attorneys

Anyone agreeing to take on the role of attorney assumes a number of duties:

- a duty of care,
- a duty not to delegate authority – he must carry out the functions personally,
- a duty not to take advantage of his position of authority,
- a duty to act in good faith and honestly,
- a duty to keep information confidential unless there is good reason to release it,
- a duty to comply with directions of the Court of Protection,
- a duty to keep accounts (for financial attorneys only) and
- a duty to keep his money separate from that of the person for whom he is attorney.

Procedure

A lasting power of attorney must conform with Schedule 1 of the Act in order for it to be valid. This requires the lasting power of attorney to contain statements by both the donor and the donee that they have read or have had read to them information about the power. The lasting power of attorney must also list any people the donor wants notified of any application to register the lasting power of attorney or, alternatively, it should state that there are no such persons.

The lasting power of attorney must also have a statement from an appropriate person (not specified in the Act itself but likely to be clarified in forthcoming regulations) indicating that at the time the donor made the power, he understood its purpose and scope. Additionally, a statement should be made that no fraud or pressure was placed upon the person when it was created. Finally, it should also state that there is no other reason why the lasting power of attorney would be invalid.

Once completed, a lasting power of attorney has to be registered with the Public Guardian. The Public Guardian will check that it meets all the necessary criteria as stated in the Act. Should the documentation have minor errors, which do not substantially affect the power, both the Public Guardian and the Court of Protection may still authorise it as valid.

Gifts

Attorneys can make gifts on behalf of the person for whom they act. The gifts must be appropriate. Birthday presents to relatives and other gifts the person may have been expected to make, including gifts to themselves and to charities are all deemed appropriate. The value of such gifts has to be reasonable in relation to the person's wealth. Gifts of substantial value may need authorisation by the Court of Protection.

Ending a lasting power of attorney

The person to whom a lasting power of attorney applies (the donor) may revoke it at any time they have capacity to do so, including after it has been registered.

In addition, an attorney loses his authority and the lasting power of attorney is ended if:

1. the attorney is disclaimed by the Lord Chancellor.
2. the attorney dies.
3. the attorney or the donor becomes bankrupt. If it is an interim bankruptcy order then the attorney and the lasting power of attorney are suspended in terms of financial affairs for as long as the order is in effect. However, this does not end the lasting power of attorney or the attorney's authority in relation to personal welfare issues.
4. the attorney is a trust and it is dissolved.
5. marriage or civil partnership between the attorney and the donor ends in divorce or annulment. However, this may have no effect if the lasting power of attorney included provision for such a situation when it was written.
6. the attorney loses capacity.

The attorney may lose their authority in the above cases but the lasting power of attorney still remains in place if it included provision for the events listed above and named a successor. Similarly, where there are two or more attorneys acting jointly or severally, if at least one attorney remains able to act and provision for such an event was made, the lasting power of attorney will remain valid.

Enduring powers of attorney

An enduring power of attorney that is in place when the Mental Capacity Act comes into force (April 2007) will have the same legal effect as before and will continue to be governed by the legal rules that applied when it was originally drawn up. See *The Public Guardian* (page 28).

Independent Mental Capacity Advocates (Sections 35-41)

Advocacy is provided for in the Act as a safeguard to certain people who lack capacity when major decisions are to be taken. Essentially the service can be seen as providing an independent review of important best interest decisions made by health and social services. At the present time, the exact remit of the advocate has yet to be finalised. Parliamentary regulations prior to April 2007 will provide clarification and may further extend the role described below.

The introduction of independent mental capacity advocates (also known by their abbreviation IMCAs) represents two fundamental changes to existing advocacy services that NHS and local authority staff may be familiar with. Firstly, the advocates have legal powers and secondly, there will be a legal duty placed on the NHS and local authorities (social services) to refer to these advocates in specific circumstances.

The advocate will be independent of health and social services and will operate within the code of practice for the Act.

Role of the advocate

At present the role of the advocate is to:

1. provide support to the person lacking capacity so that they can participate as fully as possible in any relevant decision.

2. obtain and evaluate relevant information.

3. ascertain what the person's wishes and feelings may have been and the beliefs and values that might have influenced them if they had capacity.

4. ascertain any alternative courses of action available.

Powers of the advocate

The advocate has the legal authority to:

1. interview the person he represents in private.

2. take copies of or examine any records (NHS, local authority or care home) which the record holder considers may be relevant to the advocate's role.

3. give information or make submissions to the NHS or local authority that must be taken into account.

4. obtain a further medical opinion if considered necessary (for treatment decisions).

5. challenge a proposed decision by the NHS or local authority via the Court of Protection (at the time of writing this has yet to be confirmed).

NHS and local authority duty to appoint an advocate

NHS bodies and local authorities are placed under a legal duty to instruct an advocate in any of the following circumstances where the person concerned has been assessed as lacking capacity:

1. An NHS body is proposing serious medical treatment (such treatment has yet to be precisely defined but will be prior to April 2007 in statutory regulations or the code of practice). *(Treatment under the Mental Health Act 1983, Part IV is not included.)*

    or

2. An NHS body proposes to provide accommodation in hospital for a period of more than 28 days or in a care home for more than 8 weeks. *(Accommodation provided as a result of an obligation imposed by the Mental Health Act is excluded except accommodation provided under Section 117.)*

    or

3. An NHS body proposes to change a person's accommodation to another hospital or care home for a period of more than 28 days in hospital or 8 weeks in a care home. *(Accommodation provided as a result of an obligation imposed by the Mental Health Act is excluded except accommodation provided under Section 117.)*

    or

4. A local authority proposes to provide or to change residential accommodation for more than 8 weeks continuously (*this only applies to accommodation provided under Section 21 or 29 of the National Assistance Act 1948 or Section 117 of the Mental Health Act and as a result of the local authority acting under Section 47 of the National Health Service and Community Care Act 1990. Accommodation provided as a result of an obligation imposed by the Mental Health Act is excluded).*

    AND

5. The person has no relative, friend or carer (defined here as someone not paid to care), lasting power of attorney, enduring power of attorney, deputy or individual nominated by the person lacking capacity who is appropriate to consult in determining the person's best interests.

Exceptions

If the treatment or the move to a hospital, care home or residential home needs to be provided as a matter of urgency then this may be done without consulting an advocate.

As indicated above, the NHS body or local authority does not need to appoint an advocate when a change in accommodation is likely to be less than the specified period. However, if the NHS body or local authority subsequently believes the period of time will meet the criteria above an advocate must be consulted.

Payment for Necessary Goods and Services (Section 7)

The Act allows for the supply and payment of services and goods, which are deemed "necessary" for a person lacking capacity. These must still be paid for by the person concerned (or the money can be recovered from them). For example, a milkman regularly delivering milk to a person with dementia could expect to be paid.

However, if the services or goods are not necessary then the money will not be recoverable. For example, if a builder installed double-glazing throughout a property when the replacement of one broken window would have been sufficient, the builder would be unable to recover his expenses.

Under the Act, the definition of necessary is that which is suitable to a person's "condition in life" and to his requirements at the time of supply. An item would not therefore be considered necessary under the Act if there was already an adequate existing supply.

Condition in Life

The term "condition in life" within the definition of necessary does not relate to mental or physical well being. For example food, drink and clothing are necessities for everyone. However, the quality and quantity of such essentials will depend on an individual and their circumstances.

For example, if someone has always had mineral water rather than tap water (and can afford it), they may continue to enjoy it as a necessary good under Section 7 of the Act.

Expenditure (Section 8)

If a decision-maker organises some care or treatment that involves expenditure, they can pledge the person's credit, use the person's money or reimburse themselves as necessary. For example a carer arranging the delivery of disability aids or other necessary items.

However, this does not allow the decision-maker to gain access to the person's funds if a third party such as a bank holds them. Within the scope of the Act, there is a material difference between money which is already with the person and the actual withdrawal of money from a bank account. Authority to make such withdrawals lies with a court appointed deputy, a lasting power of attorney or a single order of the Court of Protection.

There may also be an appointee under the apointeeship scheme, which gives specific authority to control social security benefits. This is under separate existing legislation, namely the Social Security (Claims and Payments) Regulations 1987 (SI 1987/1968). There is nothing to prevent an appointee also becoming a deputy under the new Act.

The Court of Protection (Sections 15-18 & 45-49)

The Court of Protection replaces the previous Court of Protection but has wider powers that reflect the scope of the Mental Capacity Act. In addition to dealing with decisions relating to property and finance as before, it will now also cover personal welfare (care and treatment) decisions, previously made by the High Court.

Role of the Court

Generally the Court will make decisions in disputed or complex circumstances regarding:

1. whether a person has capacity or lacks capacity to make a specific decision or a series of decisions.
2. the lawfulness of acts done or proposed in relation to that person, including the failure to act.
3. the validity of any lasting power of attorney or advance decision.

Where a person lacks capacity, the Court can make decisions on that person's behalf in relation to their personal welfare and financial matters, or it can appoint a deputy of the Court to make such decisions.

Remit of the Court

Court decisions on personal welfare could include:

1. where the person should live.
2. contact the person is to have with any specified people.
3. prohibiting contact with a named person.
4. giving or refusing consent to treatment.
5. the replacement of an individual responsible for the person's healthcare.

Court decisions on finances could include:

1. the control and management of property.
2. the sale, exchange, gift or other disposition of property.
3. the acquisition of property.
4. the continuation of a contract in the person's name.
5. the discharge of debts and other financial obligations.
6. the execution of a will.
7. the conduct of legal proceedings on the person's behalf.
8. the appointment of a deputy.

In addition, the Court can also make decisions on any other issues that it deems appropriate. For example, if a person loses capacity to withdraw money from their bank account, the bank would be unable to release the funds to another person unless an existing lasting power of attorney was in place or the matter was taken before the Court to make a decision.

The Court may also make decisions on the validity of a lasting power of attorney. For example, if all the requirements for creating a lasting power of attorney have been met and there is still a dispute, the Court may need to decide whether there was fraud or undue pressure placed on the person to make the lasting power of attorney. Where the attorney is not acting in the person's best interests or outside his authority the Court can revoke the lasting power of attorney.

Taking cases to the Court

It has yet to be established in which circumstances recourse to the Court will be appropriate. In some instances the matter may be too basic for the Court to intervene and it may be referred back to the parties to resolve through mediation. Evidently case law will provide some boundaries and additionally a practice direction is also expected to give guidance on this matter. The draft code of practice offers some potential examples:

- A dispute between professionals over a person's capacity to make a decision
- A dispute between family members over whether someone has capacity to make a lasting power of attorney
- A disagreement over the person appointed as attorney
- A dispute between relevant parties over whether a proposed treatment is in the person's best interests

Powers of the Court

The Court has the power to commission a report (orally or in writing) from an NHS body, local authority or care home about a person and their circumstances before they make a judgment. In addition, the Court can appoint a Court of Protection Visitor to interview the person and take copies of any records held by the NHS body, local authority or care home.

Applications to the Court

Direct applications to the Court for judgments may be made by:

- the person who lacks capacity (or is alleged to lack capacity),
- someone with parental responsibility where the person is not yet 18 years,
- a lasting power of attorney,
- a Court of Protection appointed deputy or
- a person named in an existing order of the Court.

Any other person wishing to make an application requires permission from the Court. When considering whether to give permission, the Court must consider the benefit of any proposed act and whether it can be achieved in an alternative way. It will also weigh the benefits of the proposed application against any potential distress it may cause the person lacking capacity.

Deputies (Sections 19-20)

A deputy is someone appointed by the Court of Protection to act on behalf of, and make decisions for, someone who lacks capacity. Deputies replace the existing role of receivers appointed under the former Court of Protection. They have a broader remit, which includes personal welfare (care and treatment) as well as financial affairs as previously.

Existing receivers

Receivers in place when the Mental Capacity Act comes into force (April 2007) will continue in their appointed roles, but they will then be referred to as deputies. However, the change in name for these former receivers will not mean a change in function and their duties will remain the same as when they were receivers.

Appointment of deputies

The Court may consider it necessary to appoint a deputy to manage a person's finances when there is a property to be sold or when there is a level of income or capital that requires management.

In relation to personal welfare, it is not thought that the appointment of a deputy will be required very often. However, when action cannot be taken without the need for formal powers or when there is no other way of making a decision that is in the best interests of the person lacking capacity, then the Court may appoint a deputy.

Requirements for deputies

A deputy must be at least 18 years of age. They can be the holder of a specific post or position rather than a named person. A deputy must consent to being appointed. One or more deputies can be appointed to act jointly or severally in specific matters. If acting jointly, the deputies must both agree any proposed act or decision to be made. For example, two brothers may act jointly as deputies for their father. Neither brother could therefore decide alone on their father's new care home, they would both have to agree where their father should live. If acting severally however, either one is sufficient to authorise an act or a decision.

The Court can also appoint other people to succeed existing deputies after certain events or it may appoint deputies for specified time periods.

Payment of deputies and financial issues

A deputy is entitled to claim reasonable expenses from the person's estate and, if the Court directs, receive payment for their services.

The Court can require the deputy to provide security (a deposit of money) to the Court as a means of deterring them from any wrongdoing and also to file regular accounts and reports about their activities to the Court. The Court may make specific directions in relation to these reports, for example, how detailed the reports should be and how often they should be filed.

Working With The Mental Capacity Act 2005

Where possible, the deputy must also keep their money and property separate from the finances of the person they are acting for. The draft code of practice gives a useful example of where this may not be possible. An elderly couple have always kept joint accounts and the husband is now deputy for his wife. The code envisages that in these circumstances he would not be required to separate their finances even when he becomes her deputy. Practically it would be awkward and burdensome to do this. However ultimately case law and the Court of Protection will establish the exact circumstances when this requirement may be waived.

Obligation to the Act

A deputy must comply with the principles (Section 1) and best interests (Section 4) of the Act when making decisions on behalf of the person they represent. For example they should consult, where appropriate, relatives, carers and others when making decisions, as indicated in the best interests checklist (page 9).

Powers of deputies

The deputy acts as an 'agent' for the person. Their powers are decided by the Court and can be wide-ranging, including the control and management of all or part of the person's property or more restrictive, such as deciding on a particular financial transaction.

It should be noted that a deputy cannot:

1. override the person's decision if they have capacity in relation to that decision.
2. prohibit someone from having contact with the person.
3. change the individual who is responsible for the healthcare of the person.
4. make decisions in connection with wills and trusts. These issues have to go before the Court.
5. override the authority of an existing lasting power of attorney in areas where the attorney has authority.
6. refuse consent to life-sustaining treatment for the person unless given specific authority by the Court on this issue.

Court monitoring of deputies

The Court may stop a person acting as a deputy if they are not acting in the person's best interests or if they are behaving in a way that contravenes the authority conferred on them.

The Court will decide whether the deputy has sufficient skill and expertise to discharge their particular duties. Duties will also vary depending on the deputy. For example, a solicitor or an accountant would be expected to have a higher level of duty than that of a carer.

Should a deputy believe that the person, for whom they were appointed, is now in a position to manage their own affairs, they must inform the Court. If the Court is satisfied that this is indeed true, it must end the deputy's appointment.

Working With The Mental Capacity Act 2005

The Public Guardian (Sections 57-60)

The Public Guardian replaces the existing Public Guardianship Office and has the following functions:

1. to establish and maintain a register of lasting powers of attorney,
2. to establish and maintain a register of court appointed deputies,
3. to supervise deputies,
4. to direct the work of Court of Protection Visitors,
5. to receive reports on the work of attorneys and deputies,
6. to report to the Court of Protection on matters related to the Act and
7. to deal with representations, including complaints, about the actions of attorneys or deputies.

The Lord Chancellor may add other functions at a later date.

In order to carry out this role the Public Guardian will have the power to examine and take copies of any health record, local authority record or care home record that relates to a person coming under the auspices of the Act. The Public Guardian may also interview the person in private.

The Public Guardian must write an annual report about their work for the Lord Chancellor who will, in turn, present it to Parliament.

Existing enduring powers of attorney

The Public Guardian will take over responsibility for registering enduring powers of attorney which was previously dealt with by the Public Guardianship Office. The attorney under the power can only make an application to register it if he has reason to believe that the donor has reduced capacity or will soon have reduced capacity.

Despite the Enduring Powers of Attorney Act 1985 being repealed by the new Act, existing enduring powers will continue to have effect. However, the Public Guardian will be able to cancel registration of an existing enduring power of attorney where:

1. he receives a disclaimer signed by the attorney,
2. the donor or donee dies or is made bankrupt,
3. the attorney is a corporate body and has been dissolved,
4. the Court of Protection revokes the power or
5. the Court advises that the donor has revoked the power.

The Public Guardian Board

The Board assesses the work of the Public Guardian and makes recommendations following their assessment. The Board will consist of at least one judge from the Court of Protection and four members who have appropriate knowledge or experience of the work of the Public Guardian.

Research (Sections 30-34)

The Act provides detailed rules on the requirements and procedures to be followed for intrusive research involving people who lack capacity.

Intrusive research

Intrusive research is defined as any research that requires a person's consent.

Clinical trials

A clinical trial is NOT classed as research under the Act. A clinical trial is defined as being subject to clinical trials regulations (Medicines for Human Use (Clinical Trials) Regulations 2004) and any other regulations replacing or amending these including any regulations relating to clinical trials that the Secretary of State for Health issues.

Research on people who lack capacity

Intrusive research on a person who lacks capacity to consent can only be carried out if:

1. it has been approved by an appropriate body
   and
2. consultation with carers and others has taken place
   and
3. additional safeguards are followed.

Approval

Approval must come from an appropriate body. This is defined as a person, committee or other body as specified in the regulations by the Secretary of State for Health, for example, a Research Ethics Committee.

In order to gain approval from the appropriate body, a research project must:

1. be concerned with an impairing condition affecting the person or its treatment. An impairing condition is one which causes or contributes to (or may cause or contribute to) the impairment of, or disturbance in the functioning of, the mind or brain.

and

2. have reasonable grounds for believing that research of comparable effectiveness cannot be undertaken if confined only to those who have capacity to consent.

and either

3. have the potential to benefit the person without imposing a disproportionate burden to the potential benefit.

or

4. be intended to provide knowledge of the causes, the treatment, or the care of persons affected by the same or a similar condition.

Additional information

If the fourth criterion above is met rather than the third, there must be reasonable grounds for believing that the risk to the person taking part is likely to be negligible and anything done to the person will not interfere with their freedom of activity or privacy in a significant way, or be unduly invasive or restrictive.

Consultation

The research project must take reasonable steps to identify and consult with someone involved in the care and welfare of the person, other than someone working in a professional capacity or for remuneration. However, if no such person can be found, the researcher must (as authorised by the approval body) nominate and consult a person who has no connection with the project.

The consultation process involves providing information about the research and seeking the carer's (or nominated person's) views as to whether the person lacking capacity should take part and their opinion as to the probable wishes and feelings of the person about taking part.

If the carer or nominated person feels that if the person had had capacity they would not agree to take part in the research project, it must not proceed, or it should stop if it has already started. However, if the research has already started and halting the treatment would present a significant risk to the person then the treatment can continue until such time that the risk is reduced.

Additional safeguards

If a person who lacks capacity is taking part in research then the following safeguards apply:

1. Nothing may be done to the person to which he appears to object. An exception to this is where what is being done is intended to protect him from harm or to reduce or prevent discomfort.

2. Nothing is done that is contrary to an advance decision.

3. Nothing is done that is contrary to any other form of statement made by the person.

4. The interests of the person must be assumed to outweigh those of science and society.

5. If the person indicates in any way that he wishes to withdraw from the project then his involvement must stop.

6. If the researcher has reasonable grounds for believing that any of the conditions required for approval are no longer met, the person's participation in the research must stop.

Urgent research

Urgent research may be undertaken without consulting an appropriate person if the researcher has either the agreement of a registered medical practitioner, who is not involved in the organisation or conduct of the research project, or acts in accordance with a procedure approved by the appropriate body (for example, a Research Ethics Committee).

This may be necessary when action is required immediately and it is not practicable to consult an appropriate person, for example action following a heart attack.

Once the grounds for urgency no longer apply the researcher must follow the full consultation process outlined above.

Loss of capacity during a research project

If a person with capacity consents to participating in a research project and then loses capacity before the conclusion of the research, the Research Ethics Committee or other appropriate body, may allow the person's involvement to continue. The Committee will set out conditions regarding what is required in such a situation.

Interaction with other Legislation

Mental Health Act 1983

A person may be affected by both the Mental Health Act 1983 and the Mental Capacity Act 2005 simultaneously. The most likely groups of people are those with a severe learning disability or dementia who are detained in hospital under the Mental Health Act. If decisions about their general medical care or treatment (not treatment for mental disorder) are required and the person is assessed as lacking capacity under the Mental Capacity Act then the Act could be applied to them to make a best interests decision.

If a person is detained under the Mental Health Act under a Section covered by the consent to treatment rules (treatment for mental disorder that can be given with or without consent) then the Mental Capacity Act does not apply. That is, the Mental Health Act will override the Mental Capacity Act on decisions concerning treatment for mental disorder. Consequently, there will be no requirement to go through the best interests checklist in order to come to a decision, even if the person lacks capacity.

It should be stressed that detention under the Mental Heath Act 1983 does not lead to an assumption of incapacity and the two Acts are totally independent of each other in their application.

Part 7 of the Mental Health Act 1983 is repealed with the implementation of the Mental Capacity Act 2005. This Part previously governed receivers appointed under the Mental Health Act. Section 142 of the Mental Health Act will also cease to have effect. This allowed for the government pension of a person without capacity to be paid to another party such as the institution caring for the person or the person's family. An attorney or deputy will now undertake these responsibilities. However, if the above payments have already begun, they may continue.

Children Act 1989

The Mental Capacity Act and the Children Act 1989 overlap for the 16-18 age group. Under these circumstances, the courts will decide which is the most appropriate Act to use. For example, a 17 year old with learning disabilities might be better cared for under the Mental Capacity Act, as the Children Act would no longer apply when he reached 18 but the learning disability would continue beyond this date. The Mental Capacity Act is particularly appropriate where it is expected that capacity will not be regained or attained on reaching majority. The Lord Chancellor has the power to transfer proceedings to the most appropriate court.

Enduring Powers of Attorney Act 1985

This Act will be repealed in its entirety. Lasting powers of attorney will replace enduring powers of attorney. However, any enduring powers of attorney made under the 1985 Act will continue to have effect despite its repeal. See *Lasting Powers of Attorney* (page 18) and *The Public Guardian* (page 28).

Code of Practice (Section 42)

The Lord Chancellor will issue a code of practice via Parliament concerning the operation of the Act and the roles of persons named within it, such as attorneys, deputies and advocates. However, the code is not law and the Act will always supersede the guidance given in the code of practice. Nevertheless the code can be referred to in legal proceedings. For example, in the course of any civil or criminal proceedings, the court may consider the code and any failure to comply with it when arriving at a judgment.

The code may be subject to revision from time to time.

At the time of writing a draft code of practice is available at http://www.dca.gov.uk/menincap/legis.htm#bill. Consultation on a final version will be carried out during 2006 by the Department of Constitutional Affairs and the Department of Health.

Other Matters

Limitations of the Act (Section 27)

The Act does NOT allow decisions to be made for a person lacking capacity in any of the following areas:

1. consent to marriage or civil partnership,
2. consent to sexual relations,
3. consent to divorce or dissolution of marriage or civil partnership (following two years separation),
4. consent to a child being placed for adoption or consent to making an adoption order,
5. discharge of parental responsibilities in areas not connected to a child's property and
6. consent under the Human Fertilisation & Embryology Act 1990.

The Act also makes it clear that nothing in the legislation affects existing laws relating to murder, manslaughter or assisted suicide. Consequently, an act done or decision taken under Section 4 and the best interests checklist, cannot lead to the decision to commit any of these offences.

Age Exception (Section 18(3))

The Act applies to all adults aged 16 years and over. There is an exception to this age limit for children under 16 who lack capacity and will continue to lack capacity in relation to their property and financial affairs when they reach 18 years. In such cases, the matter may be referred to the Court of Protection to make a decision on the Act's application before the age of 16.

Voting (Section 29)

The Act does NOT allow another person (including an attorney under a lasting power of attorney or a deputy) to vote on behalf of someone who lacks capacity.

Criminal Offence: ill-treatment or neglect (Section 44)

The Act creates a new criminal offence of ill-treatment or neglect. Any individual responsible for the care of a person lacking capacity (including attorneys under a lasting power of attorney or an enduring power of attorney or a deputy) who ill-treats or wilfully neglects the person is guilty of an offence and is liable to imprisonment for up to five years.

Case Studies and Examples

This section provides a number of case studies and examples that are designed to give readers of this guide an insight into the types of situation in which the Mental Capacity Act will apply. Due to the nature of each case concerning those lacking capacity, the Act cannot be totally prescriptive. It recognises its limitations however and allows for flexibility. This is demonstrated, for example, in the best interests checklist (Section 4) which provides the statutory framework for making decisions on behalf of those lacking capacity. The checklist requires the decision-maker take into account "all relevant circumstances".

When the Act comes into force and disputes arise, the Court of Protection will make judgments and these will determine the interpretation of parts of the Act that are disputed.

The application of the Act in different settings and circumstances will now be considered.

General Practice

The Act will have a considerable impact on GPs and their practices. Every practice in England and Wales provides care to people with reduced capacity, especially people with dementia and learning disabilities living in the community.

Case Study Tom lives at home with a carer and has a learning disability. He is asthmatic and needs to have his annual flu vaccination. His carer, Debbie, takes him to see his GP, Dr Samar. Every time Dr Samar tries to give Tom his vaccination, Tom moves by twisting round to look at the needle. Both Debbie and Dr Samar try to explain the importance of staying still to Tom, but he wants to see the needle every time the vaccination is attempted.

Debbie and the GP are aware of the power to restrain, using the provisions of the Act. First, they assess Tom as *lacking capacity in relation to the matter* (Section 3). Next, they assess the vaccination to be in Tom's *best interests* (Section 4) as he is asthmatic and therefore vulnerable to catching influenza. They then consider Section 6. This states that they can use restraint if they believe it is *necessary to do the act in order to prevent harm* to Tom. They agree it is necessary. Debbie simply needs to hold Tom firmly, in order to prevent him from looking around. They agree that this is a *proportionate response to the likelihood of* Tom *suffering harm* and also it is *proportionate to the seriousness of the harm* and the least restrictive option. They have a reasonable belief that Tom will find it far more painful if he moves while having the vaccination and moreover that the vaccination could be left incomplete due to his movement.

Dr Samar and Debbie conclude that Tom could come to harm if he tries to move to see the needle while having the vaccination and that a firm hold by Debbie, for a short period of time, would allow the vaccination to be completed quickly and safely. Therefore they restrain him in order to administer the vaccination.

Primary Care Trust

Primary Care Trusts (PCTs) will also be affected by the Act. They provide a broad range of services to people lacking capacity. For example:

- District nurses providing care to people with reduced capacity living at home.

- Continuing care assessments by PCT staff and subsequent decisions about the provision of care will often involve people with reduced capacity.

- Community dental services treating people lacking capacity, especially those with dementia and learning disabilities. Dental services will be required to use the Act and may make use of the power of restraint (see example above, page 35).

- Community hospitals may have continuing care wards providing for people with dementia. All care and treatment for people on the wards lacking capacity would need to follow the procedures of the Act.

- Occupational therapists working with people who lack capacity will be required to use the Act when undertaking assessments and when decisions are required regarding the provision of equipment, adaptations and services.

- Physiotherapists providing treatment to clients lacking capacity will need to make use of the Act to allow them to carry out assessments and treatment.

In all the above cases staff will have to show evidence of making assessments of capacity and best interest decisions around the provision of care or services for a person who lacks capacity.

The involvement of lasting powers of attorney with responsibility for care and treatment decisions will also have a considerable impact. The number of attorneys is likely to grow over time as the Act becomes well known by the general public.

Care Home

Any care home that has residents with dementia or learning disabilities will be directly affected by the Act. The term "personal welfare", as used in the Act, is wide-ranging and means that all personal care, such as washing, dressing and administering medication comes under the remit of the Act. Care homes will be expected to provide evidence of assessing capacity and any subsequent best interest decisions made under the Act. This is likely to be monitored by the Commission of Social Care Inspection.

<u>Case Study</u> Anne is 78 and has recently been admitted to a care home. She has dementia. When visitors come to the home Anne will often try and leave through the open doorway. Care home staff are able to talk to Anne and lead her back to the living room area.

The care home staff are aware that they are restricting Anne's *liberty of movement* (Section 6) in preventing her from leaving the home. In order for their restraint to be lawful they know they must assess whether she has *capacity in relation to the matter*. The staff assess that Anne cannot *understand the information relevant to the decision* (Section 3) regarding road safety and the possibility of getting lost (Anne is unfamiliar with the area). The staff then consider whether it is in Anne's *best interests for the act* (of restraint) *to be done*. They talk to a friend of Anne's who visits her at the home. She informs them that Anne used to spend hours in her garden pottering around when she lived at home. The care home are aware that even if the criteria for restraint are met in order to protect Anne from harm, the Act also places on them a duty for the least restrictive option in terms of a person's rights and freedom of action (Section 1).

Following the conversation with Anne's friend the staff encourage Anne to go into the garden at the rear of the home. In addition they arrange regular outings for her with staff or Anne's friend. The care home staff consider that this represents the least restrictive option and mitigates against the necessary restraint sometimes used. Even though her liberty of movement is sometimes restricted she is not deprived of her liberty, something the Act does not permit.

NHS or Foundation Trust – General Hospital

A hospital that admits any person with reduced capacity will have to follow the Act and show evidence of this. All subsequent nursing care, diagnostic tests and treatment will also come under the remit of the Act. Key areas are likely to be accident and emergency departments, wards treating people who are unconscious and wards or services treating people with dementia, learning disabilities and those who have had strokes or sustained brain injuries.

The Act also places a legal duty on Trusts proposing serious medical treatment to refer certain cases to the new independent mental capacity advocacy service.

Clinical staff are likely to see the use of advance decisions increase over time and will need to be clear about the validity of such documents as laid out in the Act.

The need to refer to and involve lasting powers of attorney, that are appointed for care and treatment decisions, is specified in the Act and again the number of attorneys in place can be expected to increase over time.

<u>Case Study</u> Victor has been in a road traffic accident and sustained a severe brain injury. He is unconscious and is put on a ventilator to assist his breathing. Without the ventilator he will not live. His daughter arrives and informs the team that she has an advance decision made by her father stating that in no circumstances would he want to be kept alive in this way. His exact words are "I only want to live if I can breath on my own – no machines."

Victor's consultant, Dr Taylor, had made a best interests decision (Section 4) for him, in an emergency situation, having assessed that he *lacked capacity in relation to the matter.* At the time the decision was taken, Dr Taylor had considered all the relevant circumstances she had been aware of. However she had not had the chance to consult with key people (Victor's daughter) and she had been unaware of his advance decision. The decision she took to put him on a ventilator was therefore the correct one at that time and her actions would be protected by the Act. However, the information presented by Victor's daughter means the decision now needs to be revised. Advance decisions supersede best interest decisions (unless a lasting power of attorney is created after the advance decision and includes authority over the decision in question). Victor's daughter is able to confirm that he has no lasting power of attorney. It is established that his advance decision, while written in lay person's terms, is valid and Victor is therefore taken off the ventilator in accordance with his wishes. (See *Advance Decisions*, page 15).

Mental Health NHS Trust

Mental health services will also need to take account of the new Act. The Mental Capacity Act 2005 can be applied to a person alongside the Mental Health Act 1983. People detained under the Mental Health Act will continue to be treated for mental disorder under that Act. However, treatment for a medical condition will come under the auspices of the Mental Capacity Act. Other patient groups, such as older people with dementia, who are often not detained under the Mental Health Act, could be treated within the remit of the Mental Capacity Act. The overlap between the two Acts has the potential to cause confusion for staff. It is likely that cases will go to court and this will help clarify the proper application of the two Acts.

The Act places a legal duty on Trusts to refer patients to the new independent mental capacity advocacy service in certain situations.

The Act provides the legal power to admit people to hospital even if they cannot consent to admission or subsequent treatment.

Case Study Mary is 74, she was admitted to an older person's mental health ward by her GP who felt she was not coping at home. She was unable to consent to the admission so her GP used the Act to carry out an assessment of her capacity and take a best interests decision. The team responsible for her care on the ward assess that she cannot return home and contact social services to arrange for her transfer to a care home. Mary has no relatives, friends or carers. Neither does she have a lasting power of attorney or another individual who could be consulted in determining her best interests. Since the move to a care home is likely to be permanent (for a period of more than 8 weeks), the team instruct the local independent mental capacity advocate.

The advocate speaks to Mary privately. He ascertains that Mary is aware she cannot return home and requires accommodation in a care home. Mary indicates to him that she wishes to move to Yorkshire where she lived as a child. (The hospital to which Mary was admitted is in London.) Whilst Mary has a diagnosis of dementia the advocate assesses that she has capacity to make the decision to move back to Yorkshire. She is able to *understand the information relevant to the decision*, *retain the information*, *use it to make a decision* and *communicate* that *decision* (Section 3). She is unable to remember the decision an hour later, however, when presented with the information again, she is consistent and makes the same decision saying, "I want to go back to Yorkshire." The team therefore ask the social worker to undertake the necessary arrangements and in due course Mary moves into a care home in Yorkshire.

Local authority (social services)

Every local authority in England and Wales will be affected by the Act as they provide a range of services involving both personal welfare (social care) and financial management for people with reduced capacity. For example:

- Social care teams undertaking assessments and deciding on packages of care will have to follow the Act when working with people who lack capacity, for example people with learning disabilities, dementia and mental health problems.

- A legal duty is placed on social services to refer cases to the new independent mental capacity advocacy service in certain situations.

- Staff involved in vulnerable adult procedures will need to take account of the Act which should help make swifter decisions for people lacking capacity, especially with regard to moving accommodation.

- A new criminal offence is created for the neglect or ill-treatment of people lacking capacity that is an imprisonable offence.

- Housing services will need to work with the Act when arranging for tenants who lack capacity to agree tenancies.

- Supported housing services will need to take the Act into account when delivering social care to clients who lack capacity.

- Members of staff may already be receivers for clients under the Mental Health Act 1983 with power to control financial affairs. With the introduction of the new Act receivers will be called deputies. Local authorities will need to consider whether they wish to expand their role to manage personal welfare decisions as allowed for by the Mental Capacity Act.

Further Information on the Act

The implementation of the Act involves both the Department of Health and the Department of Constitutional Affairs. The latter produces a monthly email bulletin on developments. For further information contact:

Mental Capacity Implementation Programme
Department of Constitutional Affairs
5th Floor
Steel House
11 Tothill Street
London SW1H 9LH

Tel: 020 7210 0037 / 0025

Fax: 020 7210 0007

Email: makingdecisions@dca.gsi.gov.uk

Website: http://www.dca.gov.uk/menincap/legis.htm#bill

At the time of writing (January 2006) the following developments are in progress:

Court of Protection – the senior judges have been appointed and the Court is preparing for April 2007. A practice direction concerning the precise nature of Court proceedings and applications to the Court will be issued prior to April next year.

Public Guardian – the Public Guardian has been appointed and is now establishing the new Office of the Public Guardian which will run in shadow form and, in due course, take over from the present Public Guardianship Office.

Code of practice – consultations are taking place on the final wording for the code of practice which will be published prior to April 2007.

Independent mental capacity advocates – a number of pilot schemes have been funded to run during 2006 which will inform the future funding, organisation and best practice of the entire service. Statutory regulations are expected that will clarify the final remit of the service.

Lasting powers of attorney – consultation is taking place on the forms and precise procedures that will govern the appointment of attorneys.

Forms – it is not clear if parliamentary regulations prior to April 2007 will provide standard wording (forms) for using the Act, especially in relation to assessment (Section 3) and best interest decisions (Section 4). If they do not, staff will have to show evidence in their records that they followed the requirements of the Act.

Sections of the Act

PART 1   **People who lack capacity**

Section

1   The principles
2   Defining capacity
3   Assessing capacity
4   Best interests (making decisions)
5   Acts in connection with care or treatment
6   Section 5 acts: limitations (restraint)
7   Payment for necessary goods and services
8   Expenditure

Lasting powers of attorney

9   Lasting powers of attorney
10   Appointment of donees
11   Restrictions on lasting powers of attorneys
12   Lasting powers of attorneys and gifts
13   Lasting powers of attorneys and revocation
14   Protection of donee and others if no power created

Court of Protection

15   Powers to make declarations
16   Powers to make decisions and appoint deputies
17   Powers relating to personal welfare
18   Powers relating to property and affairs
19   Appointment of deputies
20   Restrictions on deputies
21   Transfer of proceedings relating to people under 18

Court of Protection and lasting powers of attorney

22   Validity of lasting powers of attorney
23   Operation of lasting powers of attorney

Advance decisions

24   Advance decisions to refuse treatment
25   Validity and applicability of advance decisions
26   Effect of advance decisions

Excluded decisions

27   Family relationships etc
28   Mental Health Act matters
29   Voting rights

Working With The Mental Capacity Act 2005

Research

Independent mental capacity advocates

Miscellaneous and supplementary

PART 2   The Court of Protection and the Public Guardian

The Court of Protection

The Public Guardian

Court of Protection Visitors

PART 3   Miscellaneous and general

Schedules